Ali Ibn Abi Talib ﷺ

The Fourth Caliph of Islam

Maria Khan

Goodword

The Clan of Banu Hashim

Before the days of Islam the Arabs grouped themselves in tribes, clans and families. The Quraysh were a powerful merchant tribe that controlled Makkah and also its Kabah when the religion of Islam was founded. At the time of the Prophet Muhammad's birth, the Quraysh ruled Makkah.

The Banu Hashim was an important branch of the powerful Quraysh tribe. It takes its name from Hashim, the great-grandfather of the Prophet Muhammad.

Abdul Muttalib belonged to the clan of Banu Hashim. He was the Prophet's grandfather. He had ten sons; noteworthy among them were Abdullah, Hamza, Abbas, Abu Talib, and Abu Lahab. The house of Abdul Muttalib of Banu Hashim of Quraysh comprised a form of nobility in pre-Islamic Makkah, based upon their duty to act as stewards and caretakers of the pilgrims coming to Makkah to worship at the Kabah. This duty had been handed down to them from generation to generation.

The Prophet's father, Abdullah, died before his birth; his mother, Amina, died some seven years later. After the death of his mother, the Prophet's grandfather took care of him. But two years later Abdul Muttalib also passed away in around 578 A.D.

Abu Talib

The protection of the Prophet now fell to Abu Talib, his uncle. Despite his poverty, Abu Talib was the noblest and the most hospitable and, therefore, the most respected among the Quraysh. No wonder that the protection of young Muhammad was left to him.

Ali was born to Abu Talib in 600 A.D., ten years before the Prophet received his first revelation. Ali's mother was

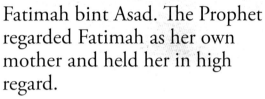

Fatimah bint Asad. The Prophet regarded Fatimah as her own mother and held her in high regard.

Apart from Ali, who was the youngest of all, Abu Talib had three sons and two daughters from his wife Fatimah bint Asad – Talib, Aqil, Jafar, Umme Hani and Jumanah.

The Prophet takes Ali into his care

Following his marriage to Khadijah, the Prophet moved out of his uncle's house and began to live with Khadijah. Khadijah was a tradeswoman of honour and great wealth. Aided by this marriage which provided amply for his needs, Muhammad spent his days respected and loved by all the people of Makkah.

Ali's stay with the Prophet dated from a time when poverty was widespread in Makkah. Since Abu Talib had a very large family, the Prophet approached his uncle Abbas, who was the richest member of the Banu Hashim clan, saying, "Your brother Abu Talib has a very large family, and he is in a state of want as a result of this widespread poverty. Let us together lighten his burden and take into our homes some of his children." Abbas agreed and took into his care Jafar, and the Prophet took Ali. Besides their own daughters, Ali, who was still a boy of five years, lived with the Prophet and Khadijah in the same house.

Ali embraces Islam

Ali, the son of Abu Talib and cousin of the Prophet, came into the Prophet's house while he and Khadijah were praying. He asked his cousin what they were doing. The Prophet told him that this was Allah's religion, the path that Allah had chosen Himself. It was to call people to this path that He had sent His prophets to the world. "Believe in One Allah," the Prophet said, "He has no partner. Worship Him alone. Forsake the idols Lat and Uzza." "I have heard nothing of this nature before today," Ali replied.

"I cannot make a decision until I have talked the matter over with my father, Abu Talib." But the Prophet did not want anyone to know about his secret until the time had come for it to be made public. "Ali," he said. "If you are not ready to become a Muslim, keep the matter to yourself." Ali waited for one night, then Allah turned his heart towards Islam. He went back to the Prophet early in the morning. "What was it that you were telling me yesterday?" he asked. "Bear witness that there is none worthy of being served save Allah. He is One. He has no partner. Forsake Lat and Uzza, and disown all those who are set up as equals with Allah." Ali did this and became a Muslim. Then, in fear of Abu Talib, he used to come and see the Prophet secretly. Ali kept his Islam a secret; he did not tell anyone about it." Ali was then the first youth to enter Islam.

Banu Hashim invited to accept the Faith

When the Prophet felt it his duty to preach in public, he became very conscious of the greatness of this task, realizing that it would require his undivided attention. He hoped that his family would look after him financially so that, freed from having to look for a livelihood; he would be able to concentrate on his preaching work. He called Abdul Muttalib's family together in his own house. There were about thirty family members at the time. The Prophet told them what his true mission in life now was. He asked for their support, so that he would be free to discharge his prophetic duties.

"Banu Abdul Muttalib," the Prophet said, "I have been sent to you in particular, and to the whole of mankind in general. Who will swear allegiance to me and become my brother and companion? Who will fulfill my debts and my promises on my behalf? Who will look after my family affairs for me? He will be with me in heaven."

The Prophet's own family was not ready to accept responsibility for him. Abbas ibn Abdul Muttalib, the Prophet's uncle, was rich enough to look after his nephew. Yet even he remained silent, for fear that this responsibility would devour his wealth. Only Ali, who was a child of about twelve years, stood up

and said, "I take your responsibility, O messenger of Allah!" On hearing Ali's response, the Prophet said, "You, O Ali, you O Ali!" None of the elders was ready to help the Prophet. Allah, however, helped His Prophet, first through the Prophet's wife, Khadijah bint Khuwaylid, and later on through Abu Bakr, whose wealth saw the Prophet through the years in Madinah.

Makkan Opposition

Some people were only familiar with religion in a particular, set form. To them, the message of Islam just appeared to put their elders in the wrong. Abu Jahl declared: "He thinks we are all fools, and considers our ancestors woefully astray. He insults our idols." "He is insane, without doubt," Umayyah added.

For some people it was the threat of financial loss, which prevented them from accepting the message of Islam. The House of Allah at Makkah had been turned into a house of idol worship before the coming of the Prophet.

People of every religion had placed their idols there. This was why four months had been made sacred – so that people would be free to visit the Kabah. During the four months that people used to flock to Makkah, Makkan traders did very good business. Were the idols to be removed from the Kabah, people would stop visiting the city, and its inhabitants would suffer immense losses. So there were many people with a stake in keeping up polytheistic practices. Thus the Quraysh became opposed to the Prophet's mission of monotheism.

Abu Talib's unswerving support for the Prophet

The Quraysh once presented a demand to the chief of the Banu Hashim, the Prophet's uncle, Abu Talib, that he should expel his nephew from the tribe. Only then would they be able to slay the Prophet. Abu Talib's honour prevented him from taking this step. When Abu Talib, at the Quraysh's behest, asked his nephew to stop criticizing their gods, the Prophet became concerned that his uncle was going to hand him over to the Quraysh. For just one moment Abu Talib hesitated between the enmity of his people and the cause of his nephew. Immediately, he called the Prophet back. "Go forth, my nephew," he said, "and say what you will. By the same Allah I swear I shall never betray you to your enemies."

Banu Hashim put under a ban

The Quraysh decided that they and all others would have nothing to do with the whole of the Banu Hashim family. A ban stopped inter-marriage and commercial relations. As a result of this boycott, the whole of the Banu Hashim clan, with the exception of Abu Lahab, were forced to live apart in a mountain ravine, called Shi'b Abi Talib.

The manner in which these people quietly endured all this cruel oppression was bound to have an effect on the conscience of others. And it did. Within three years, people like Abul Bakhtari, Hisham ibn Amr, Zubayr ibn Umayyah, Zamah ibn al-Aswad and Mut'im ibn Adi broke away from the ranks of the enemy, openly challenging this wrongful pact by which a boycott had been imposed on the Banu Hashim. The pact collapsed, and the Banu Hashim were rescued from their terrible plight.

Patience enables us to refrain from taking action, and permits things to take their natural course. Deep down, people always have a soft spot for one who bears abuse quietly, for one who refuses to be provoked even in face of the utmost provocation. The human conscience naturally tends to favour the oppressed rather than the oppressor. When the oppressed stand firm in the face of persecution, they prove themselves to be in the right. The boycott that was imposed on the Prophet and his family in the seventh year of the prophetic mission was just such an example.

Abu Talib's Death

Abu Talib became very frail due to the hardships he had to suffer during the three-year boycott. Very soon, after the boycott was lifted, he died. This was the ninth year of prophethood. At the time Ali was nineteen years old.

The tribal system prevalent in the time of the Prophet was one, which gave protection to individuals. It was seldom that anyone could survive without it. After Abu Talib's death, his responsibilities descended upon Abu Lahab. Since Abu Lahab refused to extend any protection to him, the Prophet began seeking the protection of some other tribe, so that he could continue his preaching work. Eventually Mut'im ibn Adi agreed to protect the Prophet, who, shielded by the swords of Mut'im's sons, once again entered the city walls.

Islam comes to Madinah

The people of Makkah did whatever they could to thwart the Prophet and he was subjected to torment upon

torment. Together with the Prophet, other Muslims were also persecuted in Makkah. But his mission continued to attract more and more people, and finally the message of Islam reached the people of Madinah, the majority of whom accepted Islam and agreed to give aid to the Muslims. Thus, one by one, the Muslims started emigrating to Madinah.

The Prophet's Migration and Ali's Role

Finally in 622 A.D. came the Prophet's turn. The Quraysh realized this and contrived to kill the Prophet. However, the Prophet knew exactly what was going on. Quietly, he continued his preparations. On the night of the Hijrah, the Prophet confided his plan to Ali and asked him to cover himself with his green mantle from Hadramawt and to sleep in his bed. He further asked him to tarry in Makkah until he had returned all things left with the Prophet to their rightful owners. Just before dawn, the Prophet left without being noticed.

When Ali reached Madinah the Prophet was staying at the house of Kulthum ibn Hadm. Ali went to Prophet's house to meet him. There he met the Helpers (Ansar) and other immigrants (Muhajirin). Not only did the Ansar accommodate the emigrants in their homes; they treated them as brothers and sisters, and shared their possessions with them. And they did all this, fully conscious of the fact that their action involved much more than economic sacrifice. They knew full well that what they were doing would arouse the hostility of the most powerful factions

in both Arabia and Persia. There are no words more fitting than those of Ali to describe them: "They were true to their word, steadfast in adversity."

Ali's Marriage to Fatimah

In the second year of Hijrah the Prophet married his youngest daughter Fatimah to Ali. Then, Fatimah was about eighteen years old and Ali was twenty-two. At the time of their marriage, the Prophet said to Fatimah: "I have married you to the dearest of my family to me."

Ali narrates that when he gave the proposal of marriage, the Prophet asked him, "Do you have something to give in dower (bridal gift)?" Ali confessed that he did not. The Prophet then asked, "Where is the coat of mail I gave you on so and so occasion?" Ali replied, "I have that." The Prophet said, "Give it in dower of Fatimah." Ali sold this coat for 480 dirhams and gave the dower.

Fatimah and Ali

The marriage produced three boys, Hasan, Hussain, and Muhsin (who died in his infancy) and two girls, Zainab and Umme Kulthum.

Jumai ibn Umayr once asked Aishah whom the Prophet loved most. "Fatimah," she replied. But the Prophet's whole life was moulded by thoughts of the hereafter. He loved his children, but not in any worldly way.

Ali ibn Abi Talib, Fatimah's husband, once told Ibn Abdul Wahid a story about the Prophet's most beloved daughter. Fatimah's hands, he said, were blistered from

constant grinding; her neck had become sore from carrying water; her clothes would become dirty from sweeping the floor. When the Prophet had received an influx of servants from some place, Ali suggested to his wife that she approach her father and ask for a servant. She went, but could not speak to the Prophet because of the crowd. Next day, he came to their house, and asked Fatimah why she had wanted to see him. Ali told the Prophet the whole story, and said that he had sent her. "Fear Allah, Fatimah," the Prophet said, "Fulfill your obligations to the Lord, and continue with your housework. And when you go to bed at night, praise Allah thirty-three times, and glorify Him the same number of times; exalt His name thirty-four times, and that will make a full hundred. This would be much better than having a servant." "If that is the will of Allah and His Prophet," Fatimah replied, "then so be it." This was the Prophet's only reply. He did not give her a servant.

Fatimah died six months after the Prophet's death. She was twenty-seven years old at the time of her death.

Treaty of Hudaybiyyah

The Prophet, in obedience to Allah's will, set out for Makkah in the year 6 A.H. along with 1,400 companions. He made it absolutely clear that the Muslims had no

intention of fighting anybody, and were just going for Umrah. As expected, the Quraysh advanced to prevent the Muslims from entering Makkah. The two parties met at Hudaybiyyah, some eleven kilometres from Makkah. Anxious to avoid fighting, the Prophet set up camp then and there. He then sent a message to the Quraysh, suggesting a peace treaty between the two sides. The Quraysh showed how narrowminded they were while the treaty was being compiled. The Prophet dictated to Ali: "This is a peace treaty, which Muhammad, the Messenger of Allah, has agreed upon with Suhail ibn Amr." Suhail objected saying, "Had we considered you the Messenger

of Allah, we would not have turned you away from the House of Allah, nor fought with you. You should write 'Muhammad ibn Abdullah.'" The Prophet promptly asked Ali to rub out what he had written. "By Allah, I cannot do it," replied Ali. The Prophet erased the words himself and dictated, 'Muhammad, the son of Abdullah.' Many of the clauses were more than the Companions could bear. The Muslims felt badly about the treaty.

But this truce, the terms of which appeared so against the Muslims, later brought them huge benefits.

Because of the peace which followed the Muslims gained more from the Treaty of Hudaybiyyah than from any of their campaigns. The Prophet returned to Makkah two years later with 10,000 men, whereas previously the Muslims had numbered no more than 3,000. The great lesson of Hudaybiyyah is that one should avoid impatience and should not judge matters by appearances alone. The Treaty of Hudaybiyyah which seemed so against the Muslims held great opportunities for them, which only people of insight could see.

The Importance of Dawah

Missionary activity was such an important part of the Prophet's life, that if one were to put his whole struggle under one heading, this would surely be the one. He did not concentrate on political, economic and social issues, as leaders usually do, but rather devoted his entire time and energy to preaching the word of Allah.

The Prophet Muhammad taught his companions to adopt the same attitude. It was not to be their aim to conquer territory or heap up spoils of war. Rather they were to become a source of wealth—the wealth of true faith—for others. When the Prophet entrusted Ali with the Muslim flag in the field of Khaybar, he told his cousin to proceed softly: "And when you reach their fields, call them to Islam and tell them what their responsibilities to Allah are. By Allah, if the Lord guides just one of them through you to Islam, then that will be better for you than anything upon which the sun rises."

Ali's Profound Knowledge of Islam

Ali resolved matters connected with religion and gave judgment in legal issues. This he did at a time when he was not very aged. At that time there were only a few people who knew how to read and write. Ali had learnt reading and writing from his very childhood. One of Ali's important tasks became to write letters to the people on behalf of the Prophet.

His speeches, sayings and letters were collected in Nahjul Balaghah. He was well known among the companions for his deep knowledge and understanding of the Shariah and for his ability in passing judgment on various religious matters. It was Ali who instructed Abul Aswad Duwali to frame the principles of Arabic grammar.

When Abu Bakr became caliph, he consulted Ali in important matters. Whenever he was faced with difficult problems, he called upon Ali and said: "O Abul Hasan, show us a way out of this."

After Abu Bakr, Umar became the second caliph. Ali provided the greatest support to him and helped him as a trusted advisor. There were times when Umar faced complicated issues, he would say: "We are faced with a complicated issue, but Abul Hasan is not here."

Ali was one of the electoral council, which was appointed by Umar to choose the third caliph. Finally, Uthman was selected the caliph. After Uthman's death, all the people pledged themselves to Ali ibn Abi Talib, and he therefore, became the Fourth Caliph of Islam.

Ali's Justice as Caliph

Ali at one time had a coat of armour, which he lost. One day he went to the market in Kufa, where he found that a Jew was selling a coat of armour. On closer inspection, it turned out to be the same coat of armour which he had lost.

Ali was at that time ruler of the Muslim empire. If he had so desired, he could have taken possession of that coat of armour right there and then. But he did not consider himself above the law, and merely said to the person concerned that the coat of armour belonged to him and then asked him to come to the Qazi (judge), who would decide between them. At that time Shuraih was the Qazi for Muslims. So both of them went to him.

Shuraih in the capacity of Qazi addressed Ali, "O leader of the believers, what you have to say? Ali replied, "This coat of armour is mine. So this should be returned to me." Shuraih then asked the Jew what he had to say. He said that the leader of the believers was not telling the truth for the coat of armour was his. Qazi Shuraih then said to Ali, "I cannot order the coat of armour to be given to you just because of your claim. You must fetch two witnesses in support of your claim."

Ali said that Qazi Shuraih's demand was proper. Then he presented two witnesses, one his slave Qambar and the other, his son, Hasan. Qazi Shuraih said that he would accept the testimony of Qambar, but that he would not accept that of Hasan. Ali asked, 'How is it that you will not accept Hasan as a witness, although according to a hadith the Prophet said, "Hasan and Husain are leaders of the youths of paradise."' Qazi Shuraih said: "That is a different thing. In worldly matters the principle of Islam is that evidence given by children in favour of their fathers is not reliable."

Ali being the Caliph had the power to dismiss the Qazi. But he surrendered before the judgement of the Qazi and withdrew his demand with regard to the coat of armour. On seeing this, the Jew was astonished. He exclaimed: "I bear witness it is by Allah's commandments that the leader of the believers comes to the court like a common man and the Qazi may give a verdict against him. I bear witness that there is none worthy of worship save Him and that Muhammad is the messenger of Allah." Then he said that the coat of armour really belonged to Ali

and that once, when it had fallen off Ali's camel, he had picked it up. Having heard his admission, Ali gave the coat of armour back to him and also gave him seven hundred dirhams.

This story illustrates the principle that the ruler and the ruled are equal in the eyes of the law. In a court of law both must appear on an equal footing and the legal verdict must be equally binding on both of them.

The Simple Life of Ali

Ali lived a very simple life. The many instances of his plain living, strict carrying out of religious duties, and lack of interest in worldly goods are all in record. He would always do his work with his own hands; he would not permit anyone to carry his bags for him. Even if someone went on insisting, he would not agree. If he went to buy clothes with a servant, he would first let the servant choose a garment for himself. Ali would then choose one for himself from the remaining garments.

One day, some one suggested that his clothes were not suitable for the post of a caliph. Ali's reply to this was: "A Caliph does not rule with his clothes, he rules with the responsibility and

sense of duty he feels towards Allah." "For," he explained, "these humble clothes protect me from arrogance and haughtiness."

Ali's Death

It was Friday, the seventeenth day of the month of Ramadan, 40 A.H., Ali left for the mosque for the morning prayer. It was still dark. Ibn Muljim also followed him. He quickly drew his poisonous sword and struck Ali from behind. Ali was severely wounded and finally died of the injury a few days later.

Illustrated by Gurmeet
First published 2012
Reprinted 2021
© Goodword Books 2021

Goodword Books
A-21, Sector 4, NOIDA-201301, Delhi NCR, India
Tel. +9111-41827083, Mob. +91-8588822678
email: info@goodwordbooks.com
www.goodwordbooks.com
Printed in India